THE
PILGRIMS'
PARTY

THE PILGRIMS' PARTY

A REALLY TRULY STORY
by
SADYEBETH & ANSON LOWITZ
WITH ILLUSTRATIONS BY THE LATTER

STEIN AND DAY/Publishers/New York

To BOBBIN,

that wee modern,

whose desire for

"REALLY TRULY STORIES"

inspired this book

HERE IS A REAL STORY

about real people who lived a long time before your mother, or your grandmother,—or even your great grandmother.

They were called Pilgrims. This is how they were dressed.

There were Father Pilgrims and Mother Pilgrims.
Little boy and girl Pilgrims.
Pilgrim dogs and cats.

They lived in a town with a funny name. It was SCROOBY.
Other towns in England had prettier names than Scrooby, but
the Pilgrims liked it best.

The Pilgrims were terribly good.
On Sunday they always went to church, whether it rained or not.

But where their church was, no one knew.
Not even the King's soldiers could find it.
They looked in the woods.
They looked in the cellars.
They looked in the attics.

For King James
had said that
everyone must
go to his church.
He was a frightfully
selfish man.

When the Pilgrims would not mind him, the King sent his soldiers
to Scrooby.
They took the Pilgrims away to a dark, gloomy dungeon.

There the poor Pilgrims were most uncomfortable.
For the King's dungeon was cold and damp.

Their only visitors were the big gray rats who came to eat and sleep
with them.

After several weeks, when the King thought the Pilgrims had been punished enough, he let them all go home.

Then the Pilgrims decided to run away to Holland.

So they sold their farms.   They sold their horses.
They sold their furniture and their cows and chickens.

The cows were very sad.

Pilgrim Mothers packed clothing, with a few other things in great
big trunks.
The children helped.

The next dark night, Pilgrim Fathers dragged the heavy trunks **to** the seashore.
There a boat waited which carried the Pilgrims to Holland.

Holland was not at all like SCROOBY.

Wooden shoes went
clackety, clackety-clack.

Windmills whir-r-red and
whir-r-red as 'round the
wind blew them.

Storks looked down from their nests in the chimney-tops.
And hundreds and hundreds of tulips covered the ground.

Dutch Fathers and Mothers, Dutch boys and girls, Dutch cows and chickens, all lived together in little brick houses built on legs like pianos.

Soon the Pilgrims were settled in their own little Dutch homes. Fathers worked in Dutch factories. Mothers cooked Dutch meals.

Children went to Dutch schools and played Dutch games.

The Pilgrims stayed and stayed in Holland.
They stayed so long their children turned into Dutch children.

Even their own mothers could not understand them.

This was most upsetting.
The Fathers thought and thought.

They nearly wore their heads out thinking.

One day they heard of a brand new country, America by name.

There they could build a town just like Scrooby.

But America was far across the sea and they had no boat.
So the Pilgrims saved all their pennies and bought the Speedwell.

In the ship's hold they stored barrels of grain, and bags of beans,
    and boxes of vegetables, and bottles of jam and all their belongings.
The boat got so crowded there was no room for a cow, so they filled tub
after tub with golden butter.

When all was ready, they sailed away, waving "Good-Bye" to Holland and their Dutch friends. The storks wept.

But, alas, the Pilgrims had not gone
far when their boat began to leak.

Water poured in.   Their feet got very wet.
Back they hurried for another boat.

Their new boat was bigger and better.

It was called the Mayflower.

Once more they set sail for America.

Out on the big wide ocean the waves were as high as mountains.
The wind roared and roared. The Mayflower rocked and rolled.

In fact, it was so rough, the sailors ordered the Pilgrims to remain below. One little boy disobeyed and climbed on deck just as a giant wave hit the boat. Into the sea he fell.

But he was as lucky as he was naughty. Seeing a rope from the ship
floating in the water, he grabbed it and cried for help.

Strong sailors pulled him out. He was very wet.

For days and days they sailed and sailed.
The Pilgrims played all the games they knew.

They even made up some new ones.

One dark night, way out in the middle of the ocean, a baby boy was
    born.   They named him Oceanus.
The very next night another boy was born. He was named Peregrine.

Their mothers were most surprised.

63 days went by. The Pilgrims were discouraged. Sailor after sailor climbed the mast to look for land. All they ever saw was water. One morning the smallest sailor on board was ordered to the look-out. He saw land.

He was so excited he nearly fell to the deck. While the Pilgrims, on hearing the news, threw their hats in the air and yelled for joy.

No beautiful hills like those of Scrooby greeted the Pilgrims.
Not a single house was in sight.
Tall green pines and battered oaks lined the rocky shore.

Anchoring the Mayflower, the Pilgrim Fathers set out in a life-boat to see if this place would do for their new town.

It did not take them long to decide that with so much land in America, there must surely be something better than this.

The next day was Monday. Pilgrim Mothers loaded the life-boat with tubs full of soiled clothing. There was no laundry on the Mayflower. That whole day was spent washing clothes by the side of the sea.

Ever since then, Monday has been washday in America.

Day after day they sailed along the coast looking for the very best
    place to settle.

The weather grew colder and colder. Snow began to fall.

Days were short and nights were long.

Many times Pilgrim Fathers went ashore, often remaining over night.
Once, just before daylight, they were awakened by the loud shouts and
  shrieks of wild Indians.
Arrows showered upon them. Whiz-z-z! Whiz-z-z!! Whiz-z-z!!!
Pilgrim guns answered back. Bing!! Bang!!! Boom!!!!

The Indians left in a hurry.

After nearly a month had passed by, the Mayflower came into a
beautiful harbor.

Just what the Pilgrims wanted!!

Close to the shore a big old rock seemed to welcome the Pilgrims with a smile.

They named it Plymouth Rock.

Load after load of Pilgrims left the Mayflower in the bouncing life-boat.

Out they climbed on Plymouth Rock and took a look around them.

They saw a hill for their fort. Cleared fields for their crops.
Trees for their houses. And a brook brim-full of drinking water.

Without waiting a day, the Pilgrims started to plan their town.

The first thing they did was to name it Plymouth.

As it would take too long to build a whole village at once, they built one
great big house where all could live.

From morning till night the Fathers chopped and chopped. Mothers
waxed paper for windows. There was not a piece of glass in Plymouth.

The children cut rushes to thatch the roof.

When it was finished they moved in.

Here they stayed the whole winter long.

Early in the Spring, nineteen Pilgrim Fathers started their own log houses.

They called the main street LEYDEN, after the town where they had lived in Holland. To this day it has that name.

One day while the Pilgrim Fathers were in the Town Hall, they heard
the children scream. Picking up their guns they ran to the door.
There stood a painted Indian, all by himself.

He was a very nice Indian.
His name was Samoset.

The Pilgrims liked him immensely.

In very good English, he said, "Me—Come—Help—Um."
When he left he promised to come again.

On the following Sunday, Samoset brought four of his Indian friends to see the Pilgrims. They all stayed for dinner.

The Indians had such a good time, they wanted to bring their chief the next Sunday. This pleased the Pilgrims beyond words.

For Samoset's chief was a powerful man.
He ruled MANY tribes.   His name was Massasoit.

Not many days after this, Massasoit arrived with all of his tribe. **He** brought his peace pipe with him. Everyone smoked it.

The Pilgrims and the Indians promised to be friends forever.

When Massasoit and his braves went home, one Indian boy remained
with the Pilgrims. His name was Squanto.

Once his family had lived in a wigwam just where the Pilgrim Town Hall now stood. Squanto felt at home in Plymouth.

He knew every path in the woods. He showed the Pilgrims how to trap wild animals, how to catch fish in snares, how to plant corn in hills. Squanto also taught them the Indian language.

When everyone was nicely settled in Plymouth, the Mayflower sailed back across the sea to England.

Not a single Pilgrim was on board.

The Pilgrims were still very, very good.

Every Sunday they went to church in Plymouth whether it rained or not.

There little boys and girls might whisper. Fathers and Mothers might go to sleep. But not for long. For the watchful tithingman had a stick with a feather on one end and a round knob on the other.

Those who went to sleep, he tickled with the feather.
Those who whispered, he rapped on the head.

All summer long the men worked in the fields raising grain and vegetables and big, tall corn.

The children gathered berries.

Evenings were quiet. There were no movies or radios in Plymouth.

When Fall came and the crops were harvested, the Pilgrims had twice as much food as they needed for winter.

They didn't know what to do with it all.

One of the Pilgrims suggested a Thanksgiving Party.

They would eat until their sides ached.

Everyone agreed that this was a fine idea. So a wonderful feast was planned. Squanto carried an invitation to the Indians.

They accepted with many thanks.

The Mothers baked pies, and cakes, and loaves and loaves of bread.

The children dug for clams.

The Fathers went hunting.

They brought home turkeys and deer and rabbits.

Early Thursday morning, before the Pilgrims had eaten their break-fasts, they were surprised by the wild shouts and yells of Indians. Since their guests had all arrived, the party started at once.

Ever since, Thanksgiving has come on Thursday.

Big, long picnic tables were set beneath the trees.
Everyone sat down and started to eat.
One of the Indians brought pop corn for the children.
He threw handfuls into the air.

The Pilgrims thought it was snowing.

The feast lasted for three whole days.
And such a feast it was.

Of course, they took time out to sleep.

Between meals the Indians played games.

The Pilgrim army drilled.

The little girls spilled turkey gravy all over their dress
fronts.

The little boys ate so much corn, they were butter from
ear to ear.

And when it was all over, the Indians gave three cheers for the Pilgrims. Never before had they eaten such wonderful food.

On their way home, even Massasoit, chief of all the tribes, agreed that it had been the best party he had ever attended.

THE STORY OF THE "REALLY TRULY" BOOKS

The Pilgrims' Party is one of a series of books written a generation ago by Sadyebeth and Anson Lowitz. The series was inspired by the authors' young daughter, Bobbin, who had a keen interest in hearing more about the "real" people who had lived many years ago. Other books in the "Really Truly" series include *The Cruise of Mr. Christopher Columbus, General George the Great,* and *The Magic Fountain.*

The widespread popularity of these books during the 1930's is not surprising. Here were stories very young people could understand. Mrs. Lowitz (a former teacher) and Mr. Lowitz (a busy advertising executive) used simple, straightforward language to bring historical figures alive as warmly human people.

As one generation of children grew up remembering the "Really Truly Stories," continuing requests for the books led to their re-issue. The Weekly Reader Book Club is delighted to bring you this new edition of *The Pilgrims' Party*.